This book belongs to

Katie Brokes

HAVE FUN
AND GET GLOWING!

HIGHLIGHTERS ARE THE BEST!

THEY ARE THE "BRIGHTEST" OF ALL ART SUPPLIES AND MAKE YOU SMILE JUST LOOKING AT THEM.

BUT DO YOU KNOW WHAT MAKES THEM EXTRA AWESOME?

They are TRANSLUCENT! When you use them over darker colors, they are TRANSPARENT. See how they seem to disappear into the black?

If you color over the same color it will make it darker.

You can totally color over other colors to make NEW colors and patterns. The possibilities are endless!

THIS BOOK HAS TONS OF WAYS TO USE YOUR MARKERS, AND CREATE FUN CRAFTS TOO. FOR THE CRAFTS YOU WILL NEED A FEW EXTRA SUPPLIES.

HERE ARE SOME THINGS WHICH WILL
COME IN HANDY

- ○ Permanent marker (Sharpie)
- ○ Scissors
- ○ White cloth bandage tape
- ○ Wooden clothespins
- ○ Address labels
- ○ Hole reinforcers
- ○ Empty cereal box
- ○ Elastic
- ○ Hole punch
- ○ Rubber stamps
- ○ Stamp pad
- ○ Pencils
- ○ Nail polish
- ○ Recycled containers (soup or peanut cans etc.)

GRAB YOUR MARKERS
AND LET'S GO →

COLOR LiKe CRAZY

Highlighters are **THE BEST** for coloring bold doodles. The colors disappear into the black, so you can color fast and furious!

Try it !

Grab a black permanent marker and draw some doodles of your own.

DIFFERENT PAPER = DIFFERENT LOOK
TRY YOUR HIGHLIGHTERS ON EVERYTHING.
Everything that's paper.

→ SCRIBBLE EVERYWHERE!

FIND YOUR FAVORITE

How many different patterns can you make?

Make new colors when you color over other colors.

GLOW GRID!   COLOR SHAPES IN THE GRID.

```
F  P  R  I  N  C  E  S  S  P
A  R  P  U  P  P  I  E  S  A
D  K  I  T  T  E  N  S  I  L
S  L  E  E  P  O  V  E  R  S
X  K  H  L  N  B  F  C  E  M
E  V  O  L  E  D  A  W  L  R
M  N  R  A  B  E  S  T  I  E
O  I  S  B  F  B  H  H  D  P
S  C  E  X  F  N  I  C  I  U
E  R  S  H  O  E  O  R  D  P
W  E  L  I  V  E  N  L  A  X
A  M  A  Z  I  N  G  R  K  Z
```

HIGHLIGHT THESE WORDS

AMAZING	FASHION	PRINCESS
AWESOME	FRIENDSHIP	PUPPIES
BALLET	HORSES	SHOE
BESTIE	KITTENS	SLEEPOVERS
BFF	PALS	WE

SHOE SEARCH

HIGHLIGHT WHEN YOU FIND:

20 boots-yellow

26 high heeled shoes-pink

12 flip flops-blue

9 bunny slippers-purple

WHAT DO YOU PACK FOR A SLEEPOVER?

Highlight on the list what you would definitely bring!

pillow
sleeping bag
phone
headphones
toothbrush
toothpaste
hairbrush
teddy bear
jammies
clean underwear
fuzzy slippers
socks
makeup
nail polish
snacks
cereal
candy
family photo
board games
diary

Anything missing? Add it here.

WHAT'S THE BEST?

*sleepovers at my house or *at friend's house

*sleepovers with lots of girls or *just besties

*sleepover for birthday party or *just for fun

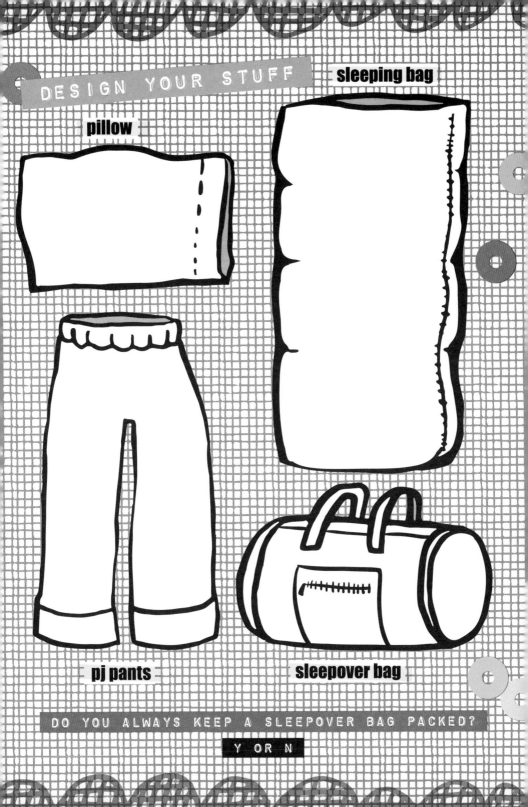

DESIGN YOUR STUFF

sleeping bag

pillow

pj pants

sleepover bag

DO YOU ALWAYS KEEP A SLEEPOVER BAG PACKED?

Y OR N

STICK-er

Color some super-bright,
super-cool stickers to bring the bling!

GRAB THIS STUFF!

STICKER SHEETS
(HOLE REINFORCERS, WHITE LABELS, ETC.)

HIGHLIGHTERS &
A PERMANENT MARKER
(OPTIONAL)

SCISSORS

Draw cool patterns on the stickers. Peel and stick!

hello

Draw pictures on bigger labels and cut them out !

Page hole reinforcers make great circle stickers.

STICK THEM ON STUFF!!!!

Decorate an envelope, a notebook, or your phone. Mark a date on the calendar or beautify a letter.

MAIL   **PLANT POTS**   **BOOKS**

This or That?

DOGS OR CATS

YOGA PANTS OR SKINNY JEANS

SNEAKERS OR HIGH HEELS

PUNK OR PREPPY

SPICY OR SALTY

EAT-IN OR EAT-OUT

SLEEP-IN OR GET UP EARLY

CAKE OR ICE CREAM

NEON OR PASTEL

ROMANCE OR COMEDY

RUN OR WALK

READ OR DRAW

MUSIC OR TV

FRIENDS OR BOYFRIEND

POPCORN OR CANDY

TYPE OR HANDWRITE

POLKA DOTS OR STRIPES

CANDY OR GUM

SHOES OR BAREFOOT

MATH OR SCIENCE

BOOK OR E-BOOK

FRIDAY OR SATURDAY

TALK OR TEXT

GLASSES OR CONTACTS

SELFIE OR GROUP PIC

DRAMA OR SCI-FI

SOCCER OR FOOTBALL

PANDA OR UNICORN

JUICE OR SODA

VIDEO GAMES OR SPORTS

BALLET OR TAP

HAMBURGER OR HOT DOG

LONG HAIR OR SHORT HAIR

HEADBAND OR BARRETTE

RAIN OR SUNSHINE

EMPTY DISHWASHER OR CLEAN ROOM

BACKPACK OR PURSE

LUNCH OR DINNER

SEE A MOVIE OR GO TO A CONCERT

ACTOR OR SINGER

STUDY OR WING IT

PONY TAIL OR BUN

CHOCOLATE OR VANILLA

BUY LUNCH OR TAKE LUNCH

CITY LIFE OR COUNTRY LIFE

This or That?

Pass your book to your friend
so she can highlight HER answers.

DOGS OR CATS

YOGA PANTS OR SKINNY JEANS

SNEAKERS OR HIGH HEELS

PUNK OR PREPPY

SPICY OR SALTY

EAT-IN OR EAT-OUT

SLEEP-IN OR GET UP EARLY

CAKE OR ICE CREAM

NEON OR PASTEL

ROMANCE OR COMEDY

RUN OR WALK

READ OR DRAW

MUSIC OR TV

FRIENDS OR BOYFRIEND

POPCORN OR CANDY

TYPE OR HANDWRITE

POLKA DOTS OR STRIPES

CANDY OR GUM

SHOES OR BAREFOOT

MATH OR SCIENCE

BOOK OR E-BOOK

FRIDAY OR SATURDAY

TALK OR TEXT

GLASSES OR CONTACTS

SELFIE OR GROUP PIC

DRAMA OR SCI-FI

SOCCER OR FOOTBALL

PANDA OR UNICORN

JUICE OR SODA

VIDEO GAMES OR SPORTS

BALLET OR TAP

HAMBURGER OR HOT DOG

LONG HAIR OR SHORT HAIR

HEADBAND OR BARRETTE

RAIN OR SUNSHINE

EMPTY DISHWASHER OR CLEAN ROOM

BACKPACK OR PURSE

LUNCH OR DINNER

SEE A MOVIE OR GO TO A CONCERT

ACTOR OR SINGER

STUDY OR WING IT

PONY TAIL OR BUN

CHOCOLATE OR VANILLA

BUY LUNCH OR TAKE LUNCH

CITY LIFE OR COUNTRY LIFE

Did you highlight any of the same things?

IT'S ALL
BLACK & WHITE

Remember the coolest thing about highlighters? **hello!** They are **AWESOME** at coloring things that are black and white!

Make copies **OR** print out your photos in black & white.
Then,
color them with the highlighters for maximum coolness!

COPY CAT

Try drawing a cool B & W pic and color it instead. ➞

Make
your mark on these photos to practice.

COLOR IS
MORE fun

IDEA

Make copies of old family photos and create a one of a kind birthday card.

"Sweet" Shoes

Design your dream sneaks

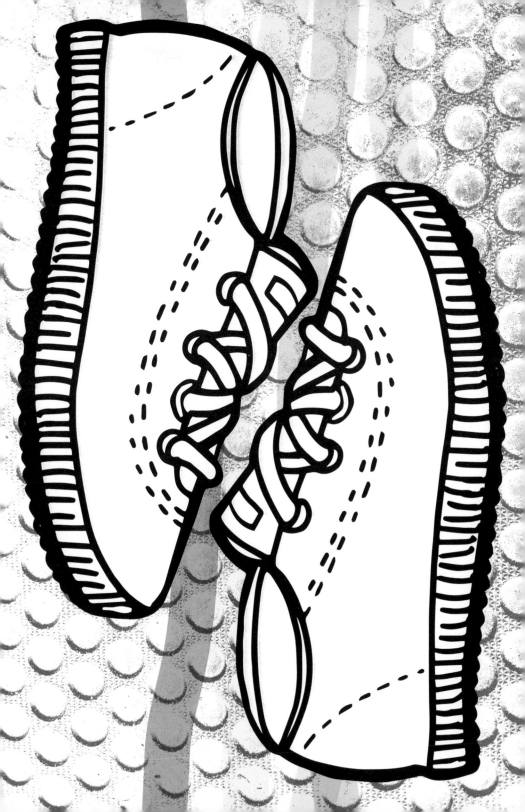

BLINGY BANGLE

ADD A LITTLE GLOW TO EVERY DAY.

Here's the DIY to make an adorable bangle. Make one for Yourself, then make more for Your friends!

GRAB THIS STUFF!

- highlighters
- cardboard cereal box
- scissors
- hole punch
- 1.5" wide white cloth tape
- 7" piece of elastic
- black Sharpie marker (optional)

IT'S BEAUTIFUL AND EARTH FRIENDLY!

❶ Cut a strip of cereal box that is 1" wide and long enough to go around your wrist.

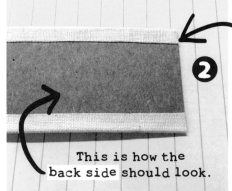

This is how the
back side should look.

2 Place the white tape
on the front of the
strip and wrap the
tape edges around
to the backside.

3 Flip the strip to
the front and color.
Let it dry.

4 Punch a hole in each
end of the strip with
hole puncher.

Then, tie the bangle
closed with the piece
of elastic.

Wear your "glow-tastic"
creation for all to see.
YOU GLOW GIRL!

How do you Glow?

Highlight your answer for each.
A's in yellow, B's in pink, and C's in blue.

1. What are your Friday night plans?
- **A.** a Movie
- **B.** the Mall
- **C.** my BFF and a sleepover

2. A friend calls and wants to hang out. You say:
- **A.** Def. I'm in the pool.
- **B.** When and where?
- **C.** I'd love to. Be right over.

3. Your school is having a dance. You will
- **A.** go with a date.
- **B.** go with friends.
- **C.** There was a dance?

**4. You sleep over at a friend's.
She wants to watch a scary movie.
What do you do?**
- **A.** Make the popcorn.
- **B.** Ask if you can watch a different movie.
- **C.** Hide your face in a pillow the entire movie.

**5. You just got home from school.
What do you do?**
- **A.** Hang out with friends.
- **B.** Grab a snack.
- **C.** Start homework.

6. What is your fave "look" in your closet?

A. tutu and funky tights
B. jeans and a black t-shirt
C. simple skirt and shirt combo

7. How do you spend your free time?

A. Get a quick mani and pedi.
B. Play your favorite video game.
C. Grab a good book.

8. When with friends at the mall, you

A. take selfies with BFF's and post them.
B. look for a new outfit.
C. do a little reading at the bookstore.

9. If you were a food, you would be a

A. spicy burrito.
B. chocolate cupcake.
C. slice of cheese pizza.

10. How would you describe yourself?

A. beautiful
B. brainy
C. quiet and shy

Add up your answers and put them here.

Turn the page for results.

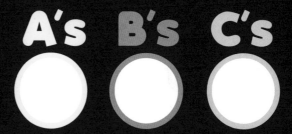

A's   B's   C's

How did it Glow?

Mostly A's.

You're neon, baby! You shine so bright,
everyone has to wear shades.

Mostly B's.

It's black and white for you girl.
There is no in-between.

Mostly C's.

You're a pastel kinda gal.
You like it a little cool and calm.

TOUGH FASHIONISTA
musical mysterious SMART
Attractive friendly famous
glowing tender brainy
TIRED HAPPY special
curious POPULAR glamorous
BRAVE different STRONG
MODERN shy I talented
sweet
Wild AM GRUMPY
FUN
SPORTY highlight who you are
thoughtful BEAUTIFUL
lazy nervous
jealous geeky FRAGILE
loner gifted smiley
ARTISTIC CREATIVE Elegant
SILLY ADVENTUROUS CUTE
MOODY bored LOYAL

AROUND AND AROUND YOU GLOW...

Get glowing

trace AROUND the shapes

DO your THING Here

play

SPOT THE DIFF'S?

Highlight the 13 diff's between the pics!

BACKPACK BLOW OUT

① **DUMP OUT YOUR BACKPACK!**

② HIGHLIGHT ANY OF THE ITEMS BELOW THAT ARE IN YOUR BACKPACK. USE THESE THREE CATEGORIES.

NORMAL   MUST HAVE   EEEW!

How did that get in there?

books	homework	picture	water bottle
paper	dead bug	moldy fruit	key chain
pencils	crayons	magazines	house key
ruler	eyeliner	erasers	
lip gloss	trash	jump drive	
smelly sock	deodorant	planner	
phone	pizza slice	calendar	
notes	gum	body spray	
washi tape	money	wad of paper	
ballpoint pen	wad of gum	chocolate goo	
lunch	permission slip	sunglasses	
candy	toothbrush	mirror	
umbrella	calculator	hair brush	

♥ Add Your own!

HOW TO:

FIRST, PAINT YOUR NAILS WITH WHITE NAIL POLISH. LET DRY.

NEXT, COLOR ON YOUR NAILS WITH HIGHLIGHTERS. LET DRY.

LAST, SEAL YOUR NAILS WITH A COAT OF CLEAR NAIL POLISH TO PROTECT YOUR DESIGNS!

ENJOY!

NEON NAILS

YOUR NAILS ARE A GREAT PLACE TO GLOW!

Color
the
shapes

A-maze-ing

Show the mama bird the
way to the baby bird.

start

Just the beginning.

(Highlight how you would complete the sentence).

After school I like to (listen to music, read a book).

A great vacation is going to (the beach, the mountains).

When I have something to say I (call, text) my friends.

My bedroom is always (totally clean, a disgusting mess).

When I sing, it is usually in the (shower, car).

My most favorite foods are (salty, sweet).

I get to school by (riding a bus, walking, car, riding a bike).

On my report card you will see (A's, B's, C's, D's).

At a party I am (the life of the party, the shy girl).

I spend too much time (watching television, texting).

I am totally a (morning person, girl of the night).

When I read it is mostly a (magazine, blog, novel).

My favorite stories are (romances, dramas, mysteries).

I prefer to watch movies at (the theater, home).

My go-to candy is (chocolate, lollipops, Skittles).

When I get mad I (cry, listen to music, call a friend).

I know how to cook (a few things, nothing at all).

When things get crazy I (stay calm, totally freak out).

Right now (I am in love, I have a crush, I am happy).

```
Y  L  D  N  E  I  R  F  U  B
G  E  N  S  H  O  N  E  S  T
E  L  E  M  S  T  Y  S  W  E
N  G  L  A  W  N  A  T  E  B
E  O  C  R  E  A  T  I  V  E
R  S  L  T  E  R  I  V  K  A
O  T  O  V  T  S  N  E  I  U
U  Y  C  E  L  E  G  A  N  T
S  L  O  D  F  U  D  E  D  I
W  I  O  O  I  U  F  U  L  F
E  S  L  O  V  I  N  G  S  U
E  H  O  R  I  G  I  N  A  L
```

FIND THESE FAB DESCRIPTIVES

CREATIVE	SMART	HONEST
BEAUTIFUL	KIND	FRIENDLY
FUN	GENEROUS	ELEGANT
SWEET	STYLISH	ORIGINAL
LOVING	FESTIVE	COOL

owl

earrings

cupcake

boot

heart

perfume

high heel

FIND THE PICS &

bird

purse

ballet shoe

leaf

bone

coin purse

lipstick

HIGHLIGHT 'EM

Room-ven-tory

How many do you have of the items below?
Highlight the amount on the glow chart.

	1	5	10	15+	20+
nail polishes					
socks					
purses					
cell phone cases					
shoes					
earrings					
hair ties & bows					
books					
markers					
lip glosses					
bracelets					
backpacks					
stuffed animals					
perfumes					
mirrors					
cute shirts					
sweaters					
hair brushes					
passwords					
journals					

MAKE YOUR MARK

and then highlight it!

GRAB THIS!

- rubber stamps
- black stamp pad
- highlighters

❶ Stamp freely and let dry, so it won't smear.

❷ Next, color in the stamps. **VOILA! INSTA-FAB!**

DID YOU KNOW you can "ink" a rubber stamp with a highlighter? Then you can highlight over that? **Crazy right? Crazy good.**

YOU TRY IT HERE.

COOL !

Just about anything can be a stamp. This is a pencil eraser and paper towel tube stamped.

FLOWER BOXES

A game for two friends to play together.

HOW TO PLAY

Each of you choose a highlighter color.

ME & YOU

Take turns drawing a line between a pair of flowers.

If your line closes a box, color the box in with your color, and go again.

Whoever creates the most boxes wins.

NEED A REMATCH? Play again.

Pretty Pencils

- highlighters
- white cloth tape
- non-stick surface (like a plastic clipboard)
- scissors
- new pencils (sharpened)

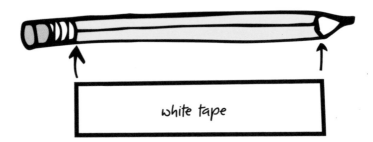

white tape

what to do

1. cut a piece of white tape this length—from the eraser to where the paint of the pencil ends.

2. place the tape down gently onto a non-stick surface. don't stick it down too hard, because you will be picking it back up in a bit.

3. color a bright pattern using the highlighters. small designs work best for wrapping a pencil.

4. when your design is completely dry, gently peel up the tape and carefully wrap it around the pencil.

Voila!

A beautifully bright pencil for happy handwriting!

what else can you make?

tiny books

colorful votives

bright markers

Fluorescent fashion!

make them gorgeous, fantastic, fabulous...
you know what to do.

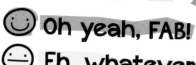 Oh yeah, FAB!

Eh, whatever.

Ugh no, DRAB!

How do you feel about the following?
Highlight the emoticon.

boys

kittens

puppies

scary movie

comedy movie

candy

nail polish

lip gloss

makeup

shopping

homework

texting

phones

pink

pizza

vegetables

sprinkles

brothers

sisters

money

sunglasses

glitter

braces

books

unicorns

ponies

TV

soda 🙂 😐 😝

birds 🙂 😐 😝

campfires 🙂 😐 😝

pants 🙂 😐 😝

skirts 🙂 😐 😝

shorts 🙂 😐 😝

this book 🙂 😐 😝

hair clips 🙂 😐 😝

curly hair 🙂 😐 😝

straight hair 🙂 😐 😝

wavy hair 🙂 😐 😝

bubbles 🙂 😐 😝

crayons 🙂 😐 😝

cotton candy 🙂 😐 😝

magazines 🙂 😐 😝

posters 🙂 😐 😝

apples 🙂 😐 😝

strawberries 🙂 😐 😝

vampires 🙂 😐 😝

washi tape 🙂 😐 😝

earrings 🙂 😐 😝

stripes 🙂 😐 😝

holidays 🙂 😐 😝

robots 🙂 😐 😝

highlighters 🙂 😐 😝

video games 🙂 😐 😝

sports 🙂 😐 😝

jeggings 🙂 😐 😝

PE 🙂 😐 😝

school lunches 🙂 😐 😝

yogurt 🙂 😐 😝

pandas 🙂 😐 😝

long car rides 🙂 😐 😝

school buses 🙂 😐 😝

popcorn 🙂 😐 😝

love 🙂 😐 😝

COLORED CLOTHESPINS

MAKE

COLORFUL PINS TO HOLD YOUR STUFF

GRAB THIS!

- wooden clothespins
- highlighters
- black Sharpie (optional)
- clear nail polish

❶ Color the clothespins. **Let them dry** between colors so they don't blend together.

❷ Add black marker to make the colors (POP). (But only if you think it looks good.)

❸ Give your masterpiece a coat of clear nail polish to seal it and add super-shine.

TOTALLY CUTE

Upstyle STORAGE

GRAB THIS!

- highlighters
- paper or self-stick labels
- scissors
- glue stick
- black Sharpie (optional)
- A clean recycled container: soup or nut cans, glass jars, candy tins, etc.

1 Cut a piece of paper or select a label which will fit your container.

2 Color a cool design onto the label or paper.

3 Carefully stick or glue your design onto the container.

now you have a bright and beautiful place to keep your treasures.

Which kitten is
different?

Color in the kitten that is different,
then color the rest of the kittens!

BAKE A CAKE ♥ RIDE A BIKE ♥ GET ALL A'S

RIDE A HORSE ♥ GET A MANICURE ♥ GO SKIING

OWN A KITTEN ♥ VISIT PARIS ♥ PLANT A TREE

RIDE A SURFBOARD ♥ MAKE A NEW FRIEND

READ A WHOLE BOOK ♥ KISS A BOY ♥ EAT SUSHI

MAKE DINNER FOR MY FAM ♥ SING IN PUBLIC

WRITE A SONG

KEEP A DIARY

GO CAMPING

START A BAND

WATER-SKI

DONE IT OR WANNA DO

COLOR YOUR COOL LIFE!

If you've done an activity, highlight it blue, if you "totes" wanna do it highlight it yellow.

MAKE ART

EAT SMORES

JOIN A CLUB

PLAY CHESS

ICE-SKATE

WRITE A LETTER TO A CELEBRITY OR STAR

SEW A PURSE ♥ HULA HOOP ♥ RUN A MILE

SKY DIVE ♥ PET A DOLPHIN ♥ BAKE COOKIES

PLAY ON A SPORTS TEAM ♥ DRIVE A CAR

PLANT A TREE ♥ GO TO A FOOTBALL GAME

VISIT LONDON ♥ HAVE A LEMONADE STAND

in ONE day

Draw a line from the **TIME OF DAY** to the **ACTIVITY** that you do at that time. It's okay to have multiple activities at one time. Hey, you're a busy girl!

eat dinner
homework
brush teeth
text friends
watch TV
check social media
feed dog/cat
call friends
clean room
hang with friends
play video games
look in the mirror
wash face
eat lunch
think about fashion
eat breakfast
brush hair
eat snack
apply lip gloss
check phone

morning

noon

evening

GLOW ON

FINISH THE PATTERNS

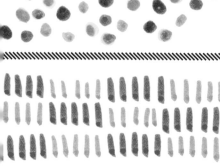

Trace your Lines

GRAB YOUR HIGHLIGHTERS &
DRAW SOME CRAZY SCRIBBLES,
SHAPES & WORDS.

NOW OUTLINE THEM WITH A PEN.

TRY USING A
COLORED PEN.

Add yours here.

Dreams follow wherever you go

BRIGHTEN SOMEONE'S DAY WITH A
NEON-TASTIC CARD

Making your own cards and stationery is
a great way to show you care!

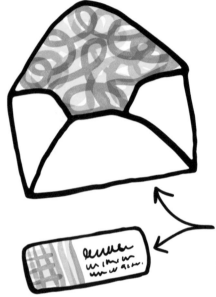

Here's a card for you
to color and send.
To get you started

WANT IT BRIGHTER?
Color some brightness on the
inside flap of the envelope
or on the address label.

ONLY TIME FOR A QUICK NOTE? Add some
bright lines or squiggles to a sticky note.
The possibilities are endlessly bright!

MADE WITH LOVE BY

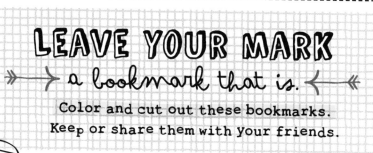

LEAVE YOUR MARK

→ *a bookmark that is.* ←

Color and cut out these bookmarks.
Keep or share them with your friends.

NOTHING TO DO HERE.

♥ this is the back of the bookmarks! ♥

COLOR
A MEGA POSTER!

The next 6 pages go together to create one large Mega-Bright-Poster to color!

HERE'S HOW TO PUT IT TOGETHER.

1. CAREFULLY tear out the next 6 pages along perforations.

2. PUT THE POSTER TOGETHER IN STRIPS.
Glue page 1 to page 2, then 3 to 4, and finally page 5 to 6.
(Use the page numbers on the back as a guide.)

NOTE: Apply the glue stick only to the areas of the poster that look grey, then overlap the pages and press together.

3. Now glue the strips of poster together from top to bottom. The back of the poster should look like this when you are finished.

4. Color and sign the poster, then hang in your room!

Be proud of yourself! You GLOW girl!

2	1
4	3
6	5

TURN THE PAGE TO START!

2

3

5

6

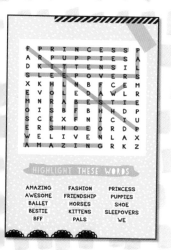

HIGHLIGHT THESE WORDS

AMAZING	FASHION	PRINCESS
AWESOME	FRIENDSHIP	PUPPIES
BALLET	HORSES	SHOE
BESTIE	KITTENS	SLEEPOVERS
BFF	PALS	WE

SPOT THE DIFF'S? Highlight the 13 diff's between the pics!

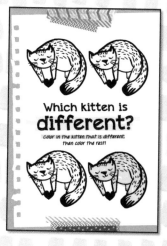

Which kitten is different?

Color in the kitten that is different, then color the rest!

A-maze-ing
Show the mama bird the way to the baby bird

start

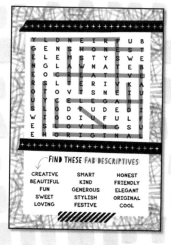

FIND THESE FAB DESCRIPTIVES

CREATIVE	SMART	HONEST
BEAUTIFUL	KIND	FRIENDLY
FUN	GENEROUS	ELEGANT
SWEET	STYLISH	ORIGINAL
LOVING	FESTIVE	COOL

SHOE SEARCH

HIGHLIGHT WHEN YOU FIND:

FIND THE PICS & HIGHLIGHT 'EM

owl, earrings, cupcake, boot, heart, perfume, high heel, bird, purse, ballet shoe, leaf, bone, coin purse, lipstick